C000001776

Sparkle World

Annual

2012

Sparkle World® Annual 2012

All of this inside...

Rainforest in my Pocket — Tropical Falls

polly pocket™

Littlest Pet Shop

Puppy in my Pocket — Enchanted Valley

Strawberry Shortcake

Ocean in my Pocket — Paradise Cove

RAINBOW magic

Group Editor: Anita Cash. Editor: Becky Mitchell
Editorial and design assistants: Louise Fell, Emma Dyson and Ella Knight.

Sparkle World® Annual 2012 is published by Redan Publishing Limited, Shrewsbury, SY3 7NR and distributed by DC Thomson Annuals Limited. **Sparkle World®** logo and **Redan** logo are trademarks of Redanco Ltd. **Littlest Pet Shop** ©2011 Hasbro. All rights reserved. Licensed by Hasbro. **My Little Pony** ©2011 Hasbro. All Rights Reserved. Licensed by Hasbro. **Polly Pocket** and associated trademarks are owned by Mattel, Inc., and used under license from Mattel Europa, B.V. ©2011 Mattel, Inc. All Rights Reserved. **Rainbow Magic** ©2011 Rainbow Magic Limited. **Strawberry Shortcake™** ©2011 Those Characters from Cleveland, Inc. Used under license by Redan Publishing Limited. **Puppy In My Pocket®, Ocean In My Pocket®** and **Pony In My Pocket®** ©2011 MEG; Puppy in My Pocket®, Ocean In My Pocket® and Pony In My Pocket® are registered trademarks of MEG. All Rights Reserved. Licensed by Licensing Works!®.

Redan Publishing is working to ensure that all its paper is produced without the use of chlorine and is sourced from well-managed forests (along the lines laid down by the Forest Stewardship Council).

Hi, Sparkle Readers!

Welcome to this jam-packed first ever Sparkle World Annual 2012! It's bursting with super sparkly things just for you! We have stories, puzzles, colouring, mazes, games and loads more with all your favourite friends, including **Rainbow Magic, Littlest Pet Shop, My Little Pony, Polly Pocket, Strawberry Shortcake** and more! Plus, we show you how to make a delicious melon crown and plan your perfect pink party! Don't forget to log on to our website, **www.mysparkleworld.com** for chances to win, as well as games, news, reviews, downloads, crafts and recipes!

Sparkly Kisses!
The Sparkle Girls
xXx

Em   Helen   Lou

Deb

It's so exciting!

www.mysparkleworld.com

Activities

Games

This super sparkly **Sparkle World** annual belongs to

....

....

Write your name here.

Redan

RAINBOW magic®

Heather the Violet Fairy!

1. Kirsty and Rachel were on holiday on Rainspell Island. They had been having fun at the fair, when they began finding the fairies. They had already found six. Jack Frost had cast a wicked spell and banished the seven Rainbow Fairies to Rainspell Island. Without the Rainbow Fairies, Fairyland had no colour! "We still have to find Heather the Violet Fairy," said Kirsty.

2. The two friends went on a carousel. It felt as if they were racing along a beach like the one painted on the ride. "Oh!" cried Kirsty. "This is like riding a real horse. It's magical!"

3. When the ride stopped, Rachel pointed to a painting on the carousel. "I think I've just found Heather," she said. "She must be trapped in the painting." "We've got to get her out!" said Kirsty.

4. "Let's use our magic bags!" said Rachel. The fairies had given the girls bags of magic gifts to help them. Kirsty felt around in hers and found a paintbrush. As she took it out, it touched the painted fairy and the whole picture glowed.

5. The fairy sprang out of the painting. The magic brush had painted Heather back to life! "Thank you for rescuing me!" said Heather. "Do you know where my Rainbow sisters are?" "Yes! Your sisters are all safe," smiled Rachel.

6. The two friends took the little fairy to where her sisters were hiding under a pot at the end of the rainbow. Izzy the Indigo Fairy saw them coming and zoomed out. "Look, everybody!" she cried. "Rachel and Kirsty have found our missing sister!" As the fairies flew up to hug and kiss Heather, the air flashed and fizzed with fairy dust! "Now that we're all together again, we must make a magic rainbow to take us back to Fairyland," said Fern the Green Fairy.

7. "Would you like to come to Fairyland?" Heather asked Kirsty and Rachel. They both nodded eagerly! Heather waved her wand, sprinkling them with purple fairy dust. The girls laughed as they turned into fairies!

8. Suddenly they heard a crackling sound. The pond at the edge of the glade was white with ice! A tall bony fairy walked into the glade. It was Jack Frost! "So you are all together again!" he hissed. "I shall never allow that!"

9. "This time we must try to stop him with a spell!" said Ruby the Red Fairy. "I know what to do!" said Sky the Blue Fairy. A jet of blue fairy dust streamed out of her wand, and trapped Jack Frost in a snow dome!

10. "Hooray for Sky!" shouted Rachel, picking up the snow dome. "Now we can take Jack Frost safely back to Fairyland!" The seven Rainbow Fairies raised their wands and a rainbow soared upwards into a clear blue sky.

11. With a whoosh the fairies shot into the sky, carried on the rainbow like a giant wave. Rachel and Kirsty felt themselves zooming up the rainbow too. "This is amazing!" Kirsty shouted. Far below they could see hillsides dotted with toadstool houses. It was Fairyland! But the hills and the toadstool houses were still grey. Kirsty and Rachel flapped their wings and drifted to the ground. One by one the Rainbow Fairies landed softly next to them.

© 2011 Rainbow Magic Limited. A HIT Entertainment Company.

12. The fairy sisters raised their wands and tiny glittering raindrops fell down around them. And where they fell the colour returned! "Now here's a special rainbow to take you home," said Heather. The fairies raised their wands again.

13. An enormous rainbow whooshed upwards! The girls whizzed back to Rainspell Island, changing to normal size on the way. "Every time I see a rainbow it will make me think of the Rainbow Fairies," said Rachel. "Me too," smiled Kirsty.

Pet Puzzles!

© 2011 Hasbro. All Rights Reserved.

1

How many of Flamingo's pink heart jewels can you count on these pages?

5

Write the number in the box.

A

2 One of the pictures of Ladybird is different. Draw a circle around it.

a

b

c

d

B

3

Can you spot 6 differences between pictures A and B? Put a tick in each flower as you find them.

4 Draw lines to match each close-up to the correct pet.

Why can't ladybirds hide?

Because they're always spotted!

a

b

c

d

e

g t a
r   y
d   r
p   f
n   f
e   r
h   e
i   i
n e d

5

Starting with the letter g, going clockwise around the flower, write every other letter in the circles below to reveal what Ladybird is looking for.

S

Answers: **Puzzle 1.** There are 6 pink heart jewels. **Puzzle 2.** Picture c is different. **Puzzle 3.** In picture B: 1. The purple flower is green. 2. The 'S' has disappeared. 3. Ladybird has moved. 4. A tomato has appeared. 5. The carrot has disappeared. 6. An orange petal is missing. **Puzzle 4.** a. Hamster, b. Monkey, c. Cat, d. Corgi. **Puzzle 5.** Garden party friends.

The Dance Show!

Using your finger, or a pencil, guide Strawberry Shortcake to Plum Pudding. Make sure you collect each pair of ballet shoes as you go.

Strawberry Shortcake is wearing an orange bow in her hair.

Tick the correct box.

True ☐   False ☑

Start

How many roses can you count in the maze?

Write your answer in the box.

5

One group of musical notes is different to the others. Circle the group that doesn't match.

Sparkle World maze

How many pairs of purple ballet shoes are there?

Write your answer in the box.

A

Finish

Strawberry Shortcake™ and related trademarks © 2011 Those Characters, From Cleveland Inc. Used under license by Redan Publishing Ltd. American Greetings with rose logo is a trademark of AGC, LLC.

AMERICAN GREETINGS

Polly pocket™

Splash Down!

Polly is visiting Splashtopia World with her friends, the Cutants! Add a splash of colour to this picture, using the small picture to help you.

How many?

Write the numbers in the boxes.

whale		1
starfish		8
crabs		5
shells		3

www.mysparkleworld.com
© 2011 Mattel, Inc. All Rights Reserved.
© 2011 Origin Products Limited.

Sparkle World colour

The Cutants have names that give hints about how they look. Circle the name of the Cutant on the list below that does not appear on these pages.

Tiki Horse

Octosub

Sharkatube

Bearabubble

Inflatafish

Rainforest in my Pocket®
Tropical Falls

A Friend for Sprinkle!

Read the story and when you see a picture, say the word instead.

Sprinkle

Floss

bush

It was a warm morning at . was keeping cool with a triple scoop ice cream! She just wished she had a best friend to enjoy it with. was a shy little capuchin and didn't know many animals. Then spotted , and sitting under a shady  . plucked up all her courage. "Hi, I'm !" she said.

"Want to join me for ice cream?" "Maybe later," said , with an enormous yawn. "We're too tired just now," said . And simply snored. He had dozed off to sleep! "I guess they don't like to make new friends," sighed , walking away.

"Of course they do," called a voice up above.

A flying dragon came gliding down from the . "Hi, ! I'm ," said the flying dragon. " , and are really friendly, but they like to play

© 2011 MEG. Rainforest in My Pocket® is a registered trademark. ALL RIGHTS RESERVED

all night and sleep all day." "Oh, so that's why they won't come out!" giggled 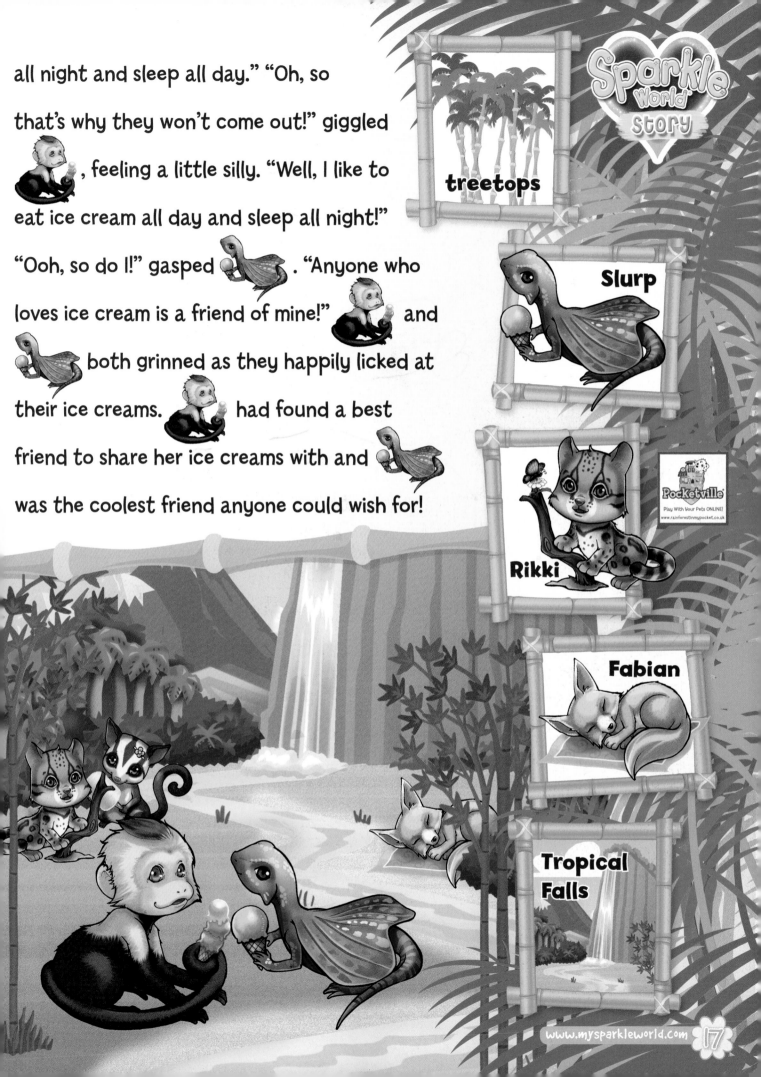, feeling a little silly. "Well, I like to eat ice cream all day and sleep all night!" "Ooh, so do I!" gasped 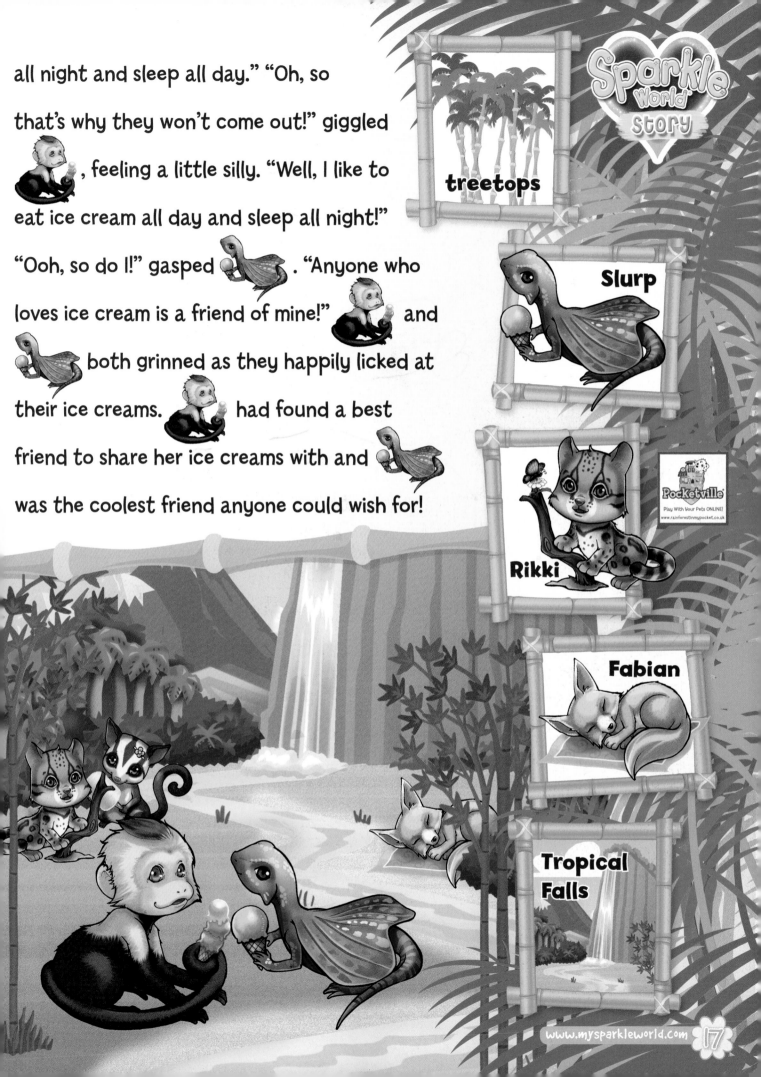. "Anyone who loves ice cream is a friend of mine!" 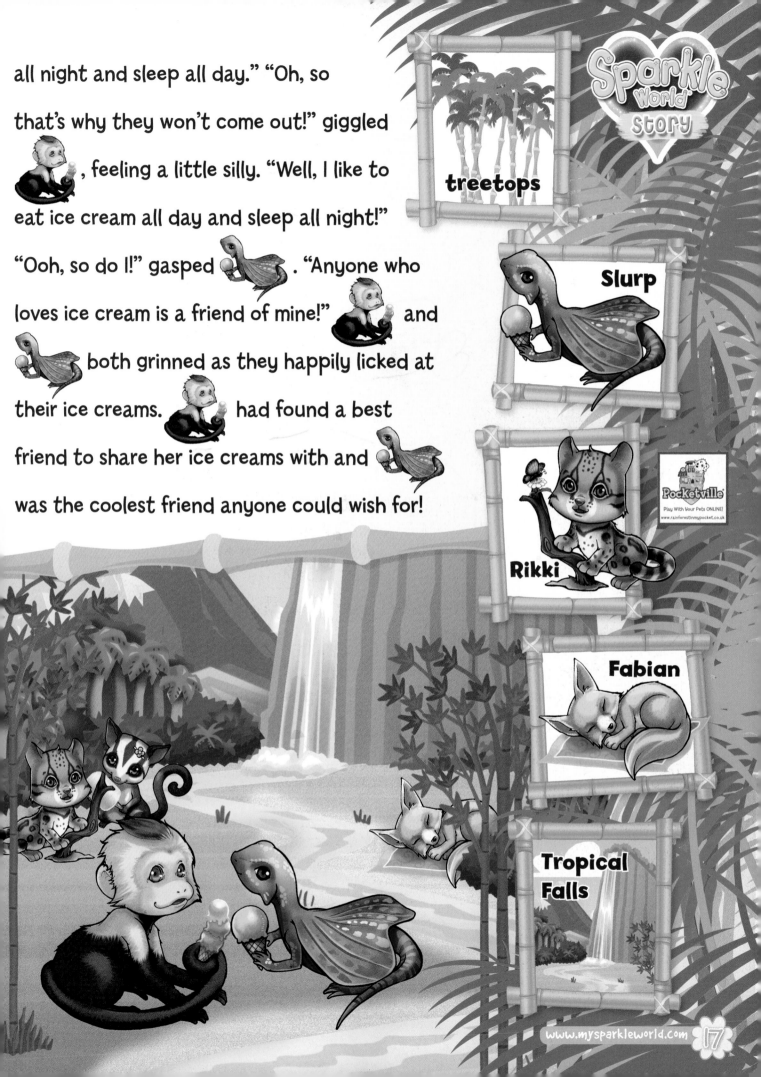 and 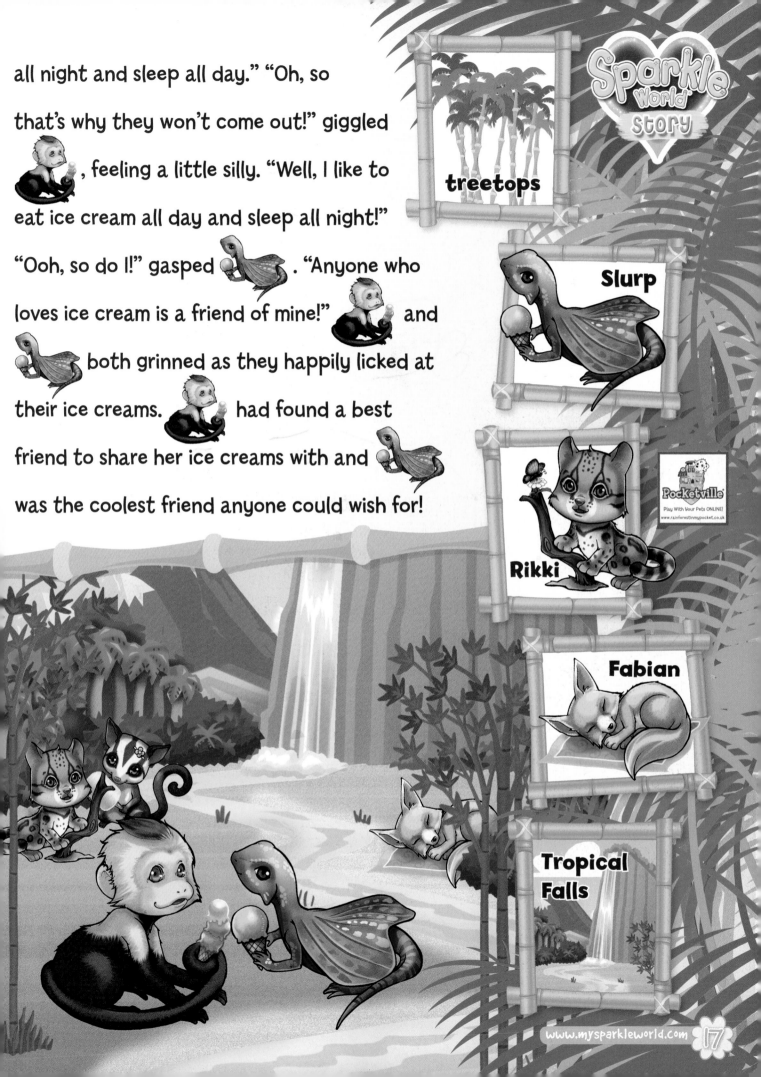 both grinned as they happily licked at their ice creams. 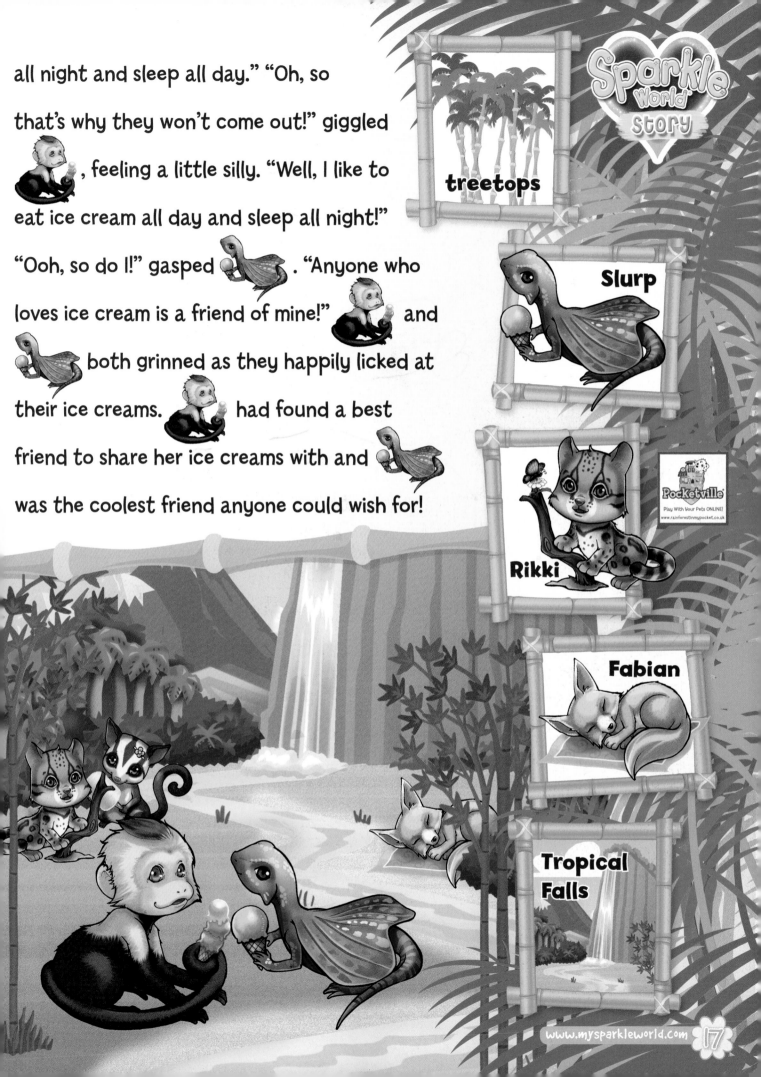 had found a best friend to share her ice creams with and 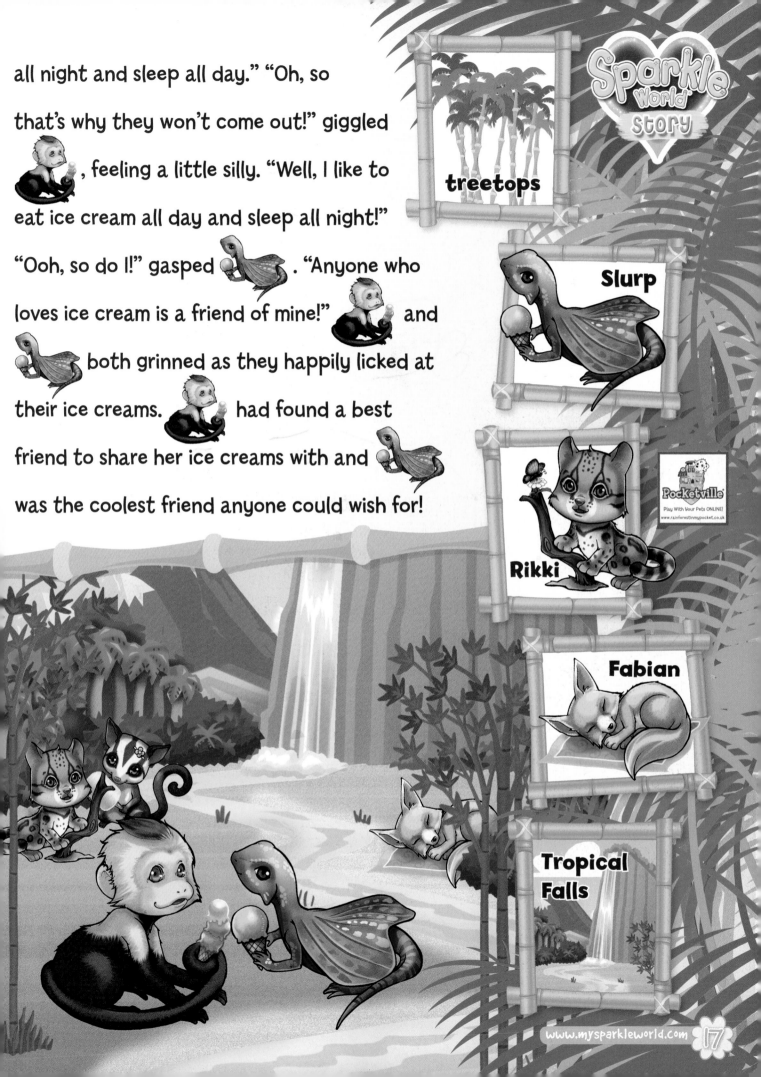 was the coolest friend anyone could wish for!

treetops

Slurp

Rikki

Fabian

Tropical Falls

Pocketville
Play With Your Pets ONLINE!
www.rainforestinmypocket.co.uk

Sparkle World® crafts & recipes!

Let's have a... Sparkly sleepover!

The Sparkle Girls are bursting with ideas to help you!

First things first! Send out some sparkletastic invitations to your friends! Why not design and make your own? We made ours out of coloured card, silk flowers, sparkly pipe cleaners and glitter glue.

A silk flower design is just right for a sleepover party!

Sleepover Party!

A handbag shape is perfect for a girlie pampering party!

Decorate the invitation with the things you plan to do.

It's party time!
Facemasks
Nails
Pamper
Pyjamas

Check out more party ideas on the Sparkle World Magazine website!

www.mysparkleworld.com

Deb's Avocado and Honey Face Mask!

Pamper your friends with Deb's sparkletastic avocado and honey face mask! It's really easy to do, so you can make it with your friends. If you'd prefer to prepare the face mask in advance, just add a squeeze of lemon juice and keep it in a sealed container in the fridge until you want to use it. Have fun!

Ingredients for one face mask:

- 2 avocados
- 2 tablespoons of plain yogurt
- 1 teaspoon of runny honey
- 2 slices of cucumber

1. Ask an adult to help you peel and mash up the flesh of two avocados in a mixing bowl.

2. Stir in the honey and yogurt to make a smooth paste.

3. Smooth a thin layer of the mixture on to your face, being careful not to get any in your eyes!

4. Place a cucumber slice over each eye. Lie back and relax for ten minutes.

5. Rinse off your face with cold water and pat your face dry with a soft towel. Your skin should feel super soft and ready for your sleepover!

Sparkletastic!

©2011 Redan.

Helen's Fab Hairstyles!

Once your face mask is off, it's time to choose from these cool hairstyles to complete your sleepover look! Take it in turns to style each other's hair.

Triple Plait

Pull your hair into a pony tail. Separate into three bunches, then plait each bunch. Secure each plait with a small bobble.

Ribbon Plait

Tie your hair in a pony tail and wrap a piece of ribbon around the bobble. Divide your hair into three sections and include the ribbon in one section. Plait your hair as normal.

Plaited Pony

Pull your hair into a pony tail and then plait it. Fold the plait up to the hair bobble and secure. Adding a flower clip completes this look!

Side Pony

Pull your hair to one side and tie in a pony tail. Don't pull all of the hair through the bobble, so it leaves the hair half tucked into the bobble. Add a flower clip! Super cute!

Plaited Buns

Divide your hair into two bunches. Plait each bunch and simply wrap around the hair bobble to create two buns. Secure with hair clips.

Em and Lou's funky nails!

You will need: A selection of nail varnishes, an emery board, hand cream and a small make-up brush.

Sleepovers are the perfect time to pamper each other and try out fab new nail designs! Take it in turns to do each other's nails.

1. Rub some hand cream into your hands and leave to soak in for five minutes. Use an emery board to smooth and shape your nails.

2. Decide on a base colour for your nails. Once painted, leave your base colour to dry completely.

3. Use a small make-up brush or paintbrush to paint a small design or pattern on top of the base coat. We like the spotty and the stripy design the best!

PONY PERSONALITIES!

Princess Celestia would like to get to know you! Tick the hearts by your seven favourite pictures, then count which colour you have the most of. This will reveal which pony you are most like.

MOSTLY ORANGE

You are down-to-earth and dependable. You're honest and never tell lies, just like Applejack.

Licensed by: © 2011 Hasbro. All Rights Reserved.

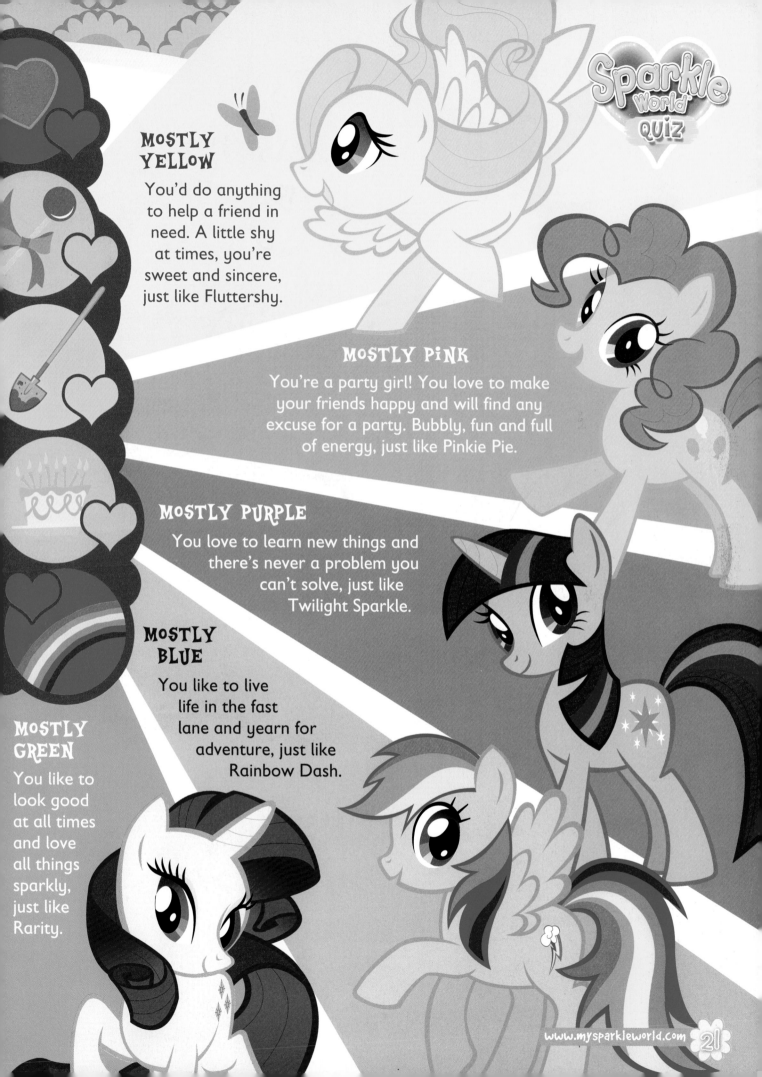

MOSTLY YELLOW

You'd do anything to help a friend in need. A little shy at times, you're sweet and sincere, just like Fluttershy.

MOSTLY PINK

You're a party girl! You love to make your friends happy and will find any excuse for a party. Bubbly, fun and full of energy, just like Pinkie Pie.

MOSTLY PURPLE

You love to learn new things and there's never a problem you can't solve, just like Twilight Sparkle.

MOSTLY BLUE

You like to live life in the fast lane and yearn for adventure, just like Rainbow Dash.

MOSTLY GREEN

You like to look good at all times and love all things sparkly, just like Rarity.

Strawberry's Family!

Around the corner, over the meadow and three steps behind the rainbow is the Enchanted Valley! It's filled with playful puppies, a gentle unicorn, fairies and other magical creatures, just like Strawberry. She's a bear with wings, and has three babies, Blueberry, Blackberry and Yellowberry.

Colour this picture using the small picture to help you.

Sparkle World COLOUR

Pocketville
Play With Your Pets ONLINE!
www.puppyinmypocket.co.uk

How many fairies can you count?

Write the number in the box.

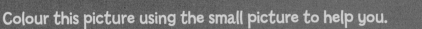

Strawberry

Blueberry

Yellowberry

Blackberry

© 2011 MEG; Puppy In My Pocket® and Enchanted Valley® are registered trademarks. ALL RIGHTS RESERVED.

Magical Memory!

Choose a fairy and spend one minute looking at her fairy things. Give this annual to your friend, then try to remember as many of the fairy's things as you can without looking. Now let your friend have a go. Whoever remembers the most is the winner!

Honey the Sweet Fairy

Grace the Glitter Fairy

Cherry the Cake Fairy

© 2011 Rainbow Magic Limited. A HIT Entertainment Company.

Another World!

Disco Bat whisks Polly and her
friends away to Electropop World!

Polly, Lila, Rick and Shani had spent the whole day at the mall. They arrived back at Polly's house totally buzzing!

"Wow, I think I bought the whole summer collection!" squealed Lila. "I need to try them out. Now!"

Lila dashed off to the bedroom and started trying on her new clothes one after another.

"Check out my new boots!" grinned Shani. "They're just perfect for my latest dance routine!"

She switched on her MP3 player, popped in the earphones and started dancing.

"That was an awesome jammin' session we had in the music shop!" grinned Rick. "It gave me a great idea for a new song!"

He borrowed Polly's guitar and started strumming and humming along.

"Er... guys?" said Polly, as her friends wandered off to do their own things. But nobody was listening.

"This is not good," said Polly to her Cutant pet, Disco Bat. "Where's the fun of hanging out with friends if they're all in a world of their own?"

Disco Bat whirred and flapped her wings. She knew exactly where to take them!

Polly gasped. "Of course!" she grinned. "You've been visiting our world but now is the perfect time to visit your world! We can all hang out there! Electropop World here we come!"

But first, Disco Bat needed to get Polly's friends to put their hands on the gadget.

"I'll help you, Disco Bat. We'll distract Rick first," Polly whispered. "Ready for 'operation friendnap'?"

Disco Bat nodded and went whirring around Rick, making him dizzy.

"Hey, watch out!" laughed Rick, waving his hands about. As he did, Polly grabbed one of his hands and put it on the gadget with hers.

"TURN IT UP!" she shouted. And a second later, they were in Electropop World.

"Huh?" gasped Rick, looking around in amazement.

Next, they went back for Lila. Luckily, Lila was doing a twirl in front of the mirror and didn't see Polly and Disco Bat sneak up behind her. Polly grabbed her hand and whisked her off to Electropop World!

"Hey!" said Lila, stunned to find herself in another world.

Last of all, was Shani. Polly danced up alongside her, pretending to join in, then grabbed her hand. In a flash they were with Disco Bat and the others.

"What's going on?" said Shani, blinking in surprise.

"Consider yourselves friendnapped by Disco Bat!" Polly told her friends. "There's no better place to sing, dance and show off your cool new style than Electropop World. So... want to hang out here with us?"

Disco Bat squeaked and waggled her wings in agreement.

"Are you kidding?" screamed Lila. "Count me in!"

"Me too!" grinned Shani and Rick.

"Now it's a party!" laughed Polly. "Take it away Z-Board!"

© 2011 Mattel, Inc All Rights Reserved. © 2011 Origin Products Limited.

Spot the Differences!

Look carefully at the two pictures below. Can you find 8 differences between them? Circle the differences in picture B as you find them.

Can you spot the hidden teddy bear?

How many pink flowers can you count?

Write the answer in the box.

© 2011 Hasbro. All Rights Reserved.

Circle the odd one out.

A.

B.

C.

D.

Sparkle World LOOK

B

Answers - no peeking!

Answers: 1. Corgi has appeared by the house; 2. The window frame has disappeared; 3. There is now a purple flower on the grass; 4. The centre of the sun is missing; 5. The gate is now blue; 6. There is no handle on the gate; 7. A ball has appeared on the path; 8. Ladybird is missing a leg. Odd one out answer: C.

PONY PUZZLES

Can you help Rainbow Dash find the words below in the wordsearch opposite? Cross out each word in the list as you find it.

DASH
PIE
PONY
FUN
FRIENDS
RARITY
FLUTTERSHY
TWILIGHT
SPARKLE
PINKIE
APPLEJACK
RAINBOW

Applejack has hidden a word in the grid opposite. Write the green letters in order in the white circles below to spell the word.

Can you help Applejack find one on this page? Colour this apple when you do.

© 2011 Hasbro. All Rights Reserved.

Sparkle World WORDSEARCH

F	L	U	T	T	E	R	S	H	Y
H	U	O	W	O	D	R	P	L	R
R	L	N	i	W	N	D	L	Y	A
A	P	P	L	E	J	A	C	K	R
i	L	O	i	W	N	S	L	V	i
N	L	N	G	N	S	H	J	N	T
B	E	Y	H	W	K	Z	P	S	Y
O	L	N	T	H	N	i	i	V	F
W	S	P	A	R	K	L	E	V	O
R	L	E	F	R	i	E	N	D	S

Answers: The hidden word is HORSESHOE.
There are 5 cupcakes, 4 diamonds and 3 crowns hidden on these pages.

Puppy in my Pocket
Enchanted Valley

© 2011 MEG. Puppy In My Pocket® and Enchanted Valley® are registered trademarks. ALL RIGHTS RESERVED

Fairy Friends!

Jade and Grace are visiting their friends, Strawberry and Tickles. Play this game with a friend to find out which fairy reaches their bear friend first!

You will need: 2 counters, a dice and a friend to play with. How to play: Choose which board you want to play on and place your counter on the Start. Take it in turns to roll the dice. If you throw an even number, move forward 2 spaces. If you throw an odd number, go back one space. The first player to reach the Finish wins!

Jade

Start

1 2 3 4 5 6 7 8 9 10 11 12 13 14 15 16 17 18 19 20 21 22 23 24 25

Finish

Strawberry

Colour Codes!

Use the key below to help you colour in the picture of Ladybird and Corgi.

How many flowers does Ladybird have on her head?

Write the answer in the box.

Key:

1 =

2 =

3 =

4 =

5 =

6 =

 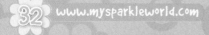 www.mysparkleworld.com

Licensed By: Littlest Pet Shop © 2011 Hasbro. All Rights Reserved.

Fruit, Fun and Friendship!

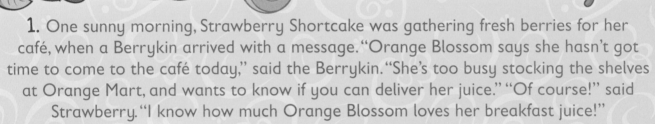

"Hi, Berrykin!"

1. One sunny morning, Strawberry Shortcake was gathering fresh berries for her café, when a Berrykin arrived with a message. "Orange Blossom says she hasn't got time to come to the café today," said the Berrykin. "She's too busy stocking the shelves at Orange Mart, and wants to know if you can deliver her juice." "Of course!" said Strawberry. "I know how much Orange Blossom loves her breakfast juice!"

"I'd do anything for you!"

2. "Thank you, Strawberry," smiled Orange, when Strawberry arrived. "It's so sweet of you to deliver my juice!" "That's okay," smiled Strawberry. "Anything for a friend!"

3. Plum Pudding was at the store. "Wow! You do a delivery service?" she asked Strawberry. "That's fantastic! Will you deliver to my dance studio?" "No problem!" agreed Strawberry.

AMERICAN GREETINGS Strawberry Shortcake™ and related trademarks © 2011 Those Characters, From Cleveland Inc. Used under license by Redan Publishing Ltd. American Greetings with rose logo is a trademark of AGC, LLC.

www.mysparkleworld.com

4. On the way to Sweet Beats studio, Strawberry bumped into Blueberry Muffin and Raspberry Torte. "Hi, Strawberry! Where are you going with that juice?" asked Blueberry. "I'm delivering to Plum's studio," explained Strawberry. "I didn't know you had started a delivery service!" gasped Blueberry. "I'm so busy today. Can you please deliver some to my store?" "And mine?" added Raspberry. "I'd be happy to," smiled Strawberry.

5. Not long after, Lemon Meringue spotted Strawberry delivering Raspberry's juice. "You do juice deliveries?" gasped Lemon. "Can I order some for my salon, please?" "I'll put you on my list," smiled Strawberry.

6. By lunchtime, Strawberry had finished all her deliveries. Berry Café was empty and there was nothing left for Strawberry to do. "I guess I should take the rest of the day off," she said, sadly. "Nobody's coming."

Oh, it's closed!

7. Meanwhile, Orange Blossom wasn't so sure she liked having her juice delivered. "It saved me time, but I really missed chatting to all my friends," she thought to herself. "It's no fun drinking juice on my own!"

8. Orange was sure all her friends must be having fun at Berry Café without her. She decided to go along and join in. But when she got there, she was amazed to find that Berry Café was closed for the day!

9. On her way home, she bumped into Raspberry, Blueberry, Plum and Lemon. "We really missed having our morning juice with Strawberry at the café," said Raspberry. "So we're all on our way there now." "It's closed," said Orange, gloomily. "And Strawberry isn't there!" "Oh!" they all gasped. "I guess we didn't realise how important Berry Café was for meeting up with all our friends," sighed Lemon. "And now we can't go at all."

10. "Hey, everybody," cried Plum. "Look! It's Custard, floating down the stream!" "Hmm! That means Strawberry won't be far away!" said Blueberry. "Come on, let's go and find her! We need our café back!"

11. They soon found Strawberry relaxing by the stream. "There you are!" said Plum. "Why isn't the café open?" "Because I don't have any customers," sighed Strawberry. "Oh yes you do!" grinned Lemon. "Us!"

12. "In that case," grinned Strawberry. "I'd be **berry** happy to open up the café!" Soon everyone was enjoying sweet treats and delicious drinks. "It was **berry** kind of you to deliver our juice, Strawberry," said Orange. "But from now on we'll be coming to the café, won't we girls?" Everyone nodded. Strawberry was delighted. After all, there was nowhere else like it for the things she liked best. Fruit, fun and friendship!

Let's make a...
Melon Crown!

Make a delicious melon crown with Sparkle Girl, Helen! It's the perfect tropical treat as part of a fruity feast!

You will need:

a honeydew melon

a selection of seasonal fruits

We used strawberries, kiwi, grapes and blueberries

a piece of string

a ruler

a pencil

An adult to help you

Wow! Delicious!

1
Ask an adult to cut about 1cm off the bottom of your melon, to give it a flat base so it can sit on a plate. Hold a piece of string around the melon and tie a knot when it sits about halfway down.

2
Use the string to help you draw a line around the melon. Use a ruler to draw triangles on this line. Ask an adult to carefully cut along the triangle shapes with a knife.

3
Once the melon has been cut all the way round, carefully pull the two halves apart. Use a spoon to scoop out the seeds, then use a melon baller to remove the flesh. Put all the melon balls to one side.

4
Ask an adult to wash and cut some of your favourite fruits into small pieces. Mix all of your fruit pieces and melon balls together in a bowl, and place back into your melon crown.

Top Tip!
Enjoy your melon crown as part of your tropical feast! Make extra bowls of fruit pieces, and serve with a delicious strawberry milkshake!

©2011 Redan.

Look and Find with the Pets!

Draw lines to match each close-up to where it fits on the big picture.

© 2011 Hasbro. All Rights Reserved.

How many apples can you count in the picture?

Write the answer in the box.

Tick a box next to each thing you find in the picture above. Circle the one that isn't there.

How many juice
cartons can you
count in the picture?

Write the answer in the box.

RAINBOW magic®

A Touch of Fairy Magic!

Use your crayons to colour this picture of the Magical Animal Fairies, using the small pictures at the bottom of the page to help you choose your colours.

Sophia
the Snow Swan Fairy

Leona
the Unicorn Fairy

© 2011 Rainbow Magic Limited.
A HIT Entertainment Company.

Put a tick in the box by your favourite Magical Animal Fairy!

Dolphin Discovery!

Tess the Dolphin is going to see her friend,
Clinger the Starfish. Follow the path through
the wave maze to show Tess the way.
Remember to collect her three dolphin babies!

Start

Tess

Siren

E

A

H

Some of the bubbles have letters hidden in them.
Write the letters in the circles below matching the
letter colours to the correct coloured circles.

Now can you find one? Draw a circle around it.

Andy

How many pearls are
in the oyster shell?
Write the number in the box.

Sparkle World maze

Grace

Finish

Clinger

© 2011 MEG. Ocean In My Pocket® is a registered trademark. ALL RIGHTS RESERVED.

Pocketville
Play With Your Pets ONLINE!
www.oceaninmypocket.co.uk

My Little Pony

PONY POWER!

When rain threatens the Apple Festival, who will save the day? Read the story and when you see a picture, say the word instead.

How many apples are in Applejack's basket? Write the number in the box.

© 2011 Hasbro. All Rights Reserved.

 Twilight Sparkle

 baked apple

Spike the Dragon

 Clouds

 and her

assistant, , were new

in Ponyville. "Hey, come to the

Apple Festival at Sweet Apple Acres

tomorrow!" said . "There'll be

s, s and lots of !"

"Wow, I'd love to!" said . But

the next day, arrived to find

looking gloomy. "It's going to

rain," sighed . "We need

to clear away the ." "Well, just

ask her," said. "I can't," said

. "She's really upset because I

didn't invite her. I meant to, but I

was so busy baking, I forgot." Just then,  spotted a rainbow-coloured glimmer in the clouds. It was ! "I guess even couldn't clear away those in time," said in a loud voice. At once, flew out of the . "Hey, I heard that!" cried . "I could clear the sky in ten seconds. Watch!" She zoomed around, bursting the and in ten seconds they were gone! "That was amazing!" gasped . "I know," grinned . And everyone laughed. "Please come to the festival, ," urged . "I was going to invite you."

chuckled. "And I was going to clear away the !"

smiled. She knew it was going to be fun living in Ponyville!

Fruit Maze!

Can you help Lemon Meringue find her way through the shape trail to Strawberry Shortcake? You can only move to the next fruit if it is the same fruit or colour. You can move up, down, left or right through the maze to the finish.

Start

Strawberry Shortcake™ and related trademarks © 2011 Those Characters, From Cleveland Inc. Used under license by Redan Publishing Ltd. American Greetings with rose logo is a trademark of AGC, LLC.

AMERICAN GREETINGS

Draw a circle around the picture of Pupcake that is the odd one out.

Finish

All About Me!

Turn these pages into your very own 'about me' profile. Fill in all of the gaps and stick photos in the special spaces! Have fun!

About Me

Name: Rebecca May Jacobs

Birthday: 10/5

Home town: Chatham

Stick a picture of you here!

My best friend is Aura

Polly wants to see who your best friend is!

Stick a picture of you both here!

Colour the flower in your favourite colour!

Food I love...

Top 5 Foods!

1. cake
2. curry
3. fruit
4. chiken
5.

My lucky number is...

3

Write the number in the box.

My happiest memory...

when I first went to All saints and meeting my sfriends

Check out www.pollypocket.co.uk

www.mysparkieworld.com © 2011 Mattel, Inc. All Rights Reserved. © 2011 Origin Products Limited.

Photo Memories - Cut and stick your favourite pictures!

Sparkle World Design

Stick your picture here!

My family!

Stick your picture here!

A fab holiday!

Stick your picture here!

A special birthday!

Circle your favourite season!

spring   summer

autumn   winter

The best place I have ever visited was...
great *galmoth*

My favourite hobby is...
Play!
one direction

My favourite band:
one Direction

My favourite song:
Call Me Maybe
Carly Rae Jepsen

Circle the words that describe you.

I am...

happy

friendly

fashionable

loud

dreamy

honest

quiet

organised   fun

My favourite flower is...
Rose

Joke Corner!

Why does a flamingo stand on one leg?

If he lifted both legs off the ground, he'd fall over!

What goes zzub zzub?

A bee flying backwards!

What do you call a cow eating grass?

A lawn-mooer!

What's black and white and red all over?

A sunburnt penguin!

What's a mouse's favourite game?

Hide and squeak!

What do you get when you cross a cat with a ball of wool?

Mittens!

What do you get if you cross a fish with an elephant?

Swimming trunks!

What do you call a sheep with no legs or head?

A cloud!

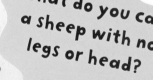

 © 2011 Hasbro. All Rights Reserved.

Royal Colours!

Colour in this picture of Princess Celestia using the small picture to help you.

HOW MANY?

Write the number in the box.

Answer: The hidden word is magic.

Five letters are hidden in the picture. Can you rearrange them to spell a word? Write them in the correct order on the lines below.

____ ____ ____ ____ ____

PRINCESS Celestia

© 2011 Hasbro. All Rights Reserved.

The Invisible Puppy

When Sassy's wish to be invisible comes true, she soon realises it has its advantages and disadvantages!

Pocketville
Play With Your Pets ONLINE!
www.puppyinmypocket.co.uk

Around the corner, over the meadow and three steps beyond the rainbow is the Enchanted Valley, filled with playful puppies and other magical creatures.

One day, Sassy the Beagle found three beautiful creatures with pointed horns playing hide and seek in the woods. They were unicorns!

"Hi, can I play?" asked Sassy, wagging her tail hopefully.

"Okay," agreed the unicorns.

One of them counted to ten, while Sassy and the other two ran off to hide. Sassy crashed noisily through the bushes and hid, giggling to herself. She was sure the little unicorn would never find her.

Suddenly, a voice behind her made her jump. "Found you!" giggled the unicorn. Sassy hadn't even heard her coming! After that, every time they played, the unicorns found her straight away.

"How do they do it?" wondered Sassy, as she ran off to hide yet again.

© 2011 MEG. Puppy in My Pocket® and Enchanted Valley® are registered trademarks. ALL RIGHTS RESERVED.

Stardust, one of the magical fairies in the Enchanted Valley, heard Sassy and flew down to answer her question. "Unicorns are so light on their feet you never hear which way they've gone," she explained. "And you never ever hear them sneaking up behind you!"

"So that's why they always win," sighed Sassy. "I wish I was invisible, then they'd never find me!"

"One wish coming up!" smiled Stardust. And with a quick swish of her wand, she made Sassy invisible.

This time, Sassy didn't even try to hide. She just stood still so that the unicorn couldn't even hear her! All afternoon the unicorn tried to find her, but with no luck.

"You win!" shouted the little unicorn. It was time for the unicorns to go home for supper.

Sassy grinned happily. At last she had won! The little puppy was hungry after hiding all that time. She headed straight for the treat tree for a tasty snack. Blueberry the flying bear was up in the tree, knocking down biscuits for the puppies to catch.

"Yoo-hoo! This way! Don't forget me!" barked Sassy, jumping up and down with the other puppies. But Blueberry couldn't even see her. She was still invisible. One by one, the puppies ran off to munch their snacks, all except Sassy.

"I don't think I like being invisible after all," sighed Sassy.

Suddenly, just like magic, Stardust appeared beside her. "I can soon fix that, little puppy," she smiled. And with a swish of her wand, she made Sassy visible again!

As soon as Blueberry saw Sassy, she threw down some treats for her to catch! The tired little puppy scampered off home. But this time she tiptoed as quietly as she could. Maybe if she practised enough, she could be as quiet as a unicorn!

RAINBOW magic®

Fairy Puzzles!

Have fun working your way through these fairytastic puzzles!

Help Saffron by drawing lines to match where each piece fits in the jigsaw.

Saffron
the Yellow Fairy

Tick the box when you find this leaf.

Read the sentences below and circle T for true or F for false.

T **Fern loves to wear green clothes.** F

T **Sky is wearing purple boots.** F

T **Izzy is wearing a silver necklace.** F

Tick the box when you find this butterfly.

The Rainbow Fairies' names are hidden in this wordsearch. Draw a line through each name and colour a flower as you find each one.

RUBY

AMBER

SAFFRON

FERN

SKY

IZZY

HEATHER

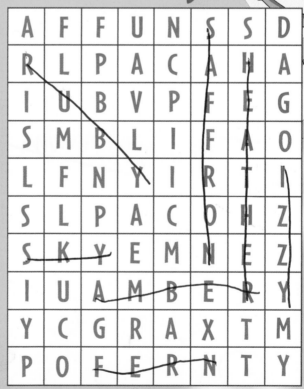

A	F	F	U	N	S	S	S	D
R	L	P	A	C	A	H	A	H
I	U	B	V	P	F	E	G	
S	M	B	L	I	F	A	O	
L	F	N	Y	I	R	T	I	
S	L	P	A	C	O	H	Z	
S	K	Y	E	M	N	E	Z	
I	U	A	M	B	E	R	Y	
Y	C	G	R	A	X	T	M	
P	O	F	E	R	N	T	Y	

Heather
the Violet Fairy

Fern
the Green Fairy

Ruby
the Red Fairy

www.mysparkleworld.com

© 2011 Rainbow Magic Limited. A HIT Entertainment Company

Izzy the Indigo Fairy has cast the wrong spell and lost her shadow! Can you help her find it? Draw a circle around the correct shadow below.

A. B. C. D. E. F.

Answer: E

Izzy
the Indigo Fairy

How many small orange flowers can you count?

Write the answer in the box.

Sky the Blue Fairy has a secret message for you. To work it out, cross out the letters that appear three times. Write the letters in order from left to right to reveal Sky's message.

m q e c b b p
p a k p q w o p
q o r c a o b r s c r h

_ _ _ _ _ _ _ _ _ _ _ _

Answer: Make a wish.

Sky
the Blue Fairy

Finish the sudoku puzzle by drawing the missing jewels in the empty heart shapes. Each jewel can appear once in each row or column.

Amber
the Orange Fairy

True or false?

Ruby has pink flowers in her hair.

T   F ✓

Tick the correct box.

Rainforest in my Pocket — Tropical Falls

A game for 2 players.

Rainforest Race!

Bali the Silvery Marmoset is going to meet Chill the Bonobo by Tropical Falls. Play this game with a friend to see who gets there first!

Bali
Silvery
Marmoset

1 start

2

3 Colour three flowers for Vanilla the Anteater. Move on 2 spaces.

4 Sing a song in a funny monkey voice, then move on 1 space.

5

6 Papaya the Toucan comes for a visit. Go back to the start!

7

8 Stop to have an ice cream with Sprinkle the Capuchin. Miss a turn!

9 Relax in the sun with Coconut, the Red Frog. Go back 2 spaces.

10 Move your counter to the same space as your friend!

11

12 Slurp the Flying Dragon has lost two ice creams. Move on 2 spaces when you find one.

13

14

15

16 Think of an animal beginning with the same letter as your name, then move on 3 spaces.

You will need: 2 counters, a dice and a friend to play with.
How to play: Place your counters on the Start. Take it in turns to roll the dice and move your counters along the path. The first player to reach the finish is the winner!

Sparkle World game

Pocketville
Play With Your Pets ONLINE!
www.rainforestinmypocket.co.uk

17 Do a monkey dance with Mikey the Macaque! Move on 2 spaces.

26

25

27 Sunny the Mandrill shares his smoothie with you! Move on 1 space.

18 Have a snooze with the sloth. Miss a turn!

28

24 Roddie the Gecko clings to you as you swing through the trees. Move on 2 spaces.

19

23

29 Finish

20 If your name begins with a vowel, A, E, I, O or U, move back one space.

22

21 Build a sandcastle with Lexi the Iguana. Roll again!

Chill Bonobo

© 2011 MEG; Rainforest In My Pocket® is a registered trademark. ALL RIGHTS RESERVED.

Mix and Match!

Read the clues then draw lines to match each one to Strawberry or her friends.

Answers: Clue 1: Plum Pudding, shadow a; Clue 2: Raspberry Torte, shadow b; Clue 3: Blueberry Muffin, shadow f; Clue 4: Orange Blossom, shadow e; Clue 5: Strawberry Shortcake, shadow d; Clue 6: Lemon Meringue, Shadow c.

Clue 1
Dancing makes me so happy, I just have to dance when I hear music.

Clue 2
I love to give fashion tips to all the girls so they look super stylish!

Clue 3
I love reading and learning about how things work. I am a friend to rely on.

Strawberry Shortcake

Blueberry Muffin

Orange Blossom

Now draw lines to match Strawberry and her friends to their shadowy shapes.

a   b   c

How many?

Write the numbers in the boxes.

3 | 23 | 4 | 3

Sparkle World PUZZLE

AMERICAN GREETINGS

Strawberry Shortcake™ and related trademarks © 2011 Those Characters. From Cleveland Inc. Used under license by Redan Publishing Ltd. American Greetings with rose logo is a trademark of AGC, LLC.

Clue 4
My favourite thing to do is go shopping with my berry best friends!

Clue 5
I am lucky to have such berrylicious friends! They often turn to me for advice.

Clue 6
I'm bright and cheerful like the sun! I also love to have lots of fun.

Lemon Meringue

Raspberry Torte

Plum Pudding

d

e

f

1. Pet Town was buzzing with excitement! There was going to be a talent show and all the pets were busy rehearsing. All except Boy Monkey. He had always dreamed of being a rock star. Every time he heard music he just couldn't resist dancing and sometimes, when no one was looking, he would twang a guitar. But he just wasn't sure he was very good at it!

Littlest Pet Shop © 2011 Hasbro. All Rights Reserved.
Licensed by: Hasbro

2. Boy Monkey went and found a quiet spot to listen to his music by himself. It wasn't long before he had to start dancing along to the rhythm. He just couldn't help it!

3. Suddenly, something went whizzing past his ear, knocking his hat off. It was Ladybird! "Sorry!" she giggled. "I'm practising my act. I'm going to do an aerobatic show."

4. "Hey, want to see me loop the loop?" said Ladybird. Before he could answer, she zoomed up high then flew upside-down, making a circle in the sky. "Wow!" gasped Boy Monkey.

5. But Ladybird got dizzy and crashed into a flower patch. "Oops!" she giggled. "I'm sure I'll get the hang of it before the show." And she flew away, still giggling.

6. Boy Monkey went to the playground, hoping it would be safer. Suddenly, Corgi came charging up chasing a runaway ball. "Stop that ball!" yapped Corgi. Boy Monkey caught it and tossed it to the pup. Corgi flipped it in the air with his nose and balanced it on top of his head! "That's so cool!" laughed Boy Monkey. "Is that your act for the talent show?"

7. Corgi nodded in agreement, and the ball rolled away again. "Uh-oh, there it goes again!" he chuckled. "I'm always doing that!" "But don't you mind if you make a mistake?" asked Boy Monkey. "Of course not," laughed Corgi. "The important thing is to have fun! Excuse me! I've got to go and catch that ball!" And he scampered away.

8. "Nobody seems to mind if things go a bit wrong," thought Boy Monkey. "They just have fun trying!" Just then, he heard a strange noise coming from the pet café.

9. Cat, Hamster and Flamingo were all trying to play guitars. But it sounded awful. "It's no good," sighed Flamingo. "We're good at singing but none of us can play guitar."

10. "We can't be a rock band without a guitar player," grumbled Cat, "but we don't know anyone who can play." Without thinking, Boy Monkey leapt out shouting, "I can!"

11. "That's great!" grinned Cat. "Come on, the show's about to start!" Boy Monkey blinked in surprise. He was going to be in the show after all. And he didn't mind one little bit!

12. TWANNGGGG! Boy Monkey leapt on stage, and everyone gasped. He couldn't just play one guitar. He could play two at a time! The whole crowd went bananas! No one even noticed when he played a wrong note now and again. Everyone was too busy dancing and having fun. Especially Boy Monkey! His dream had come true at last. He was a rock star!

Let's make some... Sparkletastic Gifts!

Sparkle Girl, Lou, will show you how to make a cute glove buddy and a pretty plant pot gift for your friends and family!

Glove Buddy!

Funky Flowerpot!

You will need:

safety scissors
a pair of old gloves
buttons
googly eyes
PVA glue
needle and cotton
stuffing
elastic band
An adult to help you!

1.
Ask an adult to help you make the head by carefully cutting the two middle fingers off one glove. Tuck the thumb in on itself. Stitch up the holes where the fingers were. Stuff the glove with stuffing.

2. On the second glove, tuck in the thumb, first and little finger. Carefully stitch the holes closed to stop the fingers coming back out.

3. Stitch back on the two fingers you cut off to make the arms. Stuff the second glove and the fingers to make the legs. Tie off the second glove with an elastic band, and slide the first glove on top. Add button and googly eyes, a button nose and tongue to complete your glove buddy!

You will need:

safety scissors
kitchen sponge
acrylic paint
potting compost
small clay pot (9cm)
flower seeds
sparkly pipe cleaners
plastic gems
An adult to help you!

1. Ask an adult to carefully cut a heart shape out of the kitchen sponge. Dip it in your favourite colour paint and stamp the sides of your pot. You can decorate it with some plastic gems to make your pot sparkle. Leave your pot to dry.

2. Tie two sparkly pipe cleaners around the top of your pot to add more sparkle. Fill your pot with potting compost and decide on what seeds you would like to plant. Push them into the soil. Why not put your pot in a small cellophane bag and tie it up with ribbon before you give it as a gift?

©2011 Redan.

Best Friends Forever!

What kind of relationship do you have with your best friend? Find out with Polly and Lila.

How to play:

Sit opposite your friend with the Sparkle World Annual between you. With a pencil, answer the questions by colouring the flower by your answer. Turn the Annual round and count how many answers your friend got right. Then check your friendship score.

Check out www.pollypocket.co.uk.

My friend's most splenderific colour is ...

Her favourite food is ...

The thing we most love to do together is ...

Watch a movie   Make cakes   Sing songs

If she could have any cutant pet it would be ...

Meowmallow   Disco Bat   Bearabubble

She would love to try ...

Skydiving   Quadbiking   Rollerblading

www.mysparkleworld.com

Your friendship score!

5

You are a perfect pair! You have fun together and share everything!

Polly's Tip: Make friendship bracelets for each other.

3-4

You know each other well, but both have other close friends.

Polly's Tip: Join a club together. You may be surprised what you learn!

0-2

True friendship takes time but don't give up.

Polly's Tip: Throw a sleepover party and share all your secrets! You'll soon be getting 5 out of 5!

© 2011 Mattel, Inc. All Rights Reserved.
© 2011 Origin Products Limited.

My friend's most splenderific colour is ...

Her favourite food is ...

The thing we most love to do together is ...

Watch a movie

Make cakes

Sing songs

If she could have any cutant pet it would be ...

Meowmallow

Disco Bat

Bearabubble

She would love to try ...

Skydiving

Quadbiking

Rollerblading

Cameo the Chameleon

Cameo the Chameleon loves to float down the river on his lilo. Colour the picture using the small picture to help you.

Sparkle World COLOUR

Pocketville
Play With Your Pets ONLINE!
www.rainforestinmypocket.co.uk

Rainforest in my Pocket®
Tropical Falls

How many Rainforest In My Pocket friends can you count altogether on this page?
Write the number in the box.

© 2011 MEG. Rainforest In My Pocket® is a registered trademark. ALL RIGHTS RESERVED

Sending Secrets!

Twilight Sparkle and Spike the Dragon have a secret message for Princess Celestia. Can you crack the code to reveal what it says?

Dear Princess Celestia

The most

powerful

magic of

all is

friendship!

From Twilight Sparkle and Spike

Answer: The most powerful magic of all is friendship!

KEY:

A -
B -
C -
D -
E -
F -
G -
H -
I -
J -
K -
L -
M -
N -
O -
P -
Q -
R -
S -
T -
U -
V -
W -
X -
Y -
Z -

Licensed By: Hasbro © 2011 Hasbro. All Rights Reserved.

www.mysparkleworld.com 69

Ocean Friends!

Discover which of the Ocean In My Pocket creatures you are most like! Answer the questions and follow the arrows to find out!

Start

Is your idea of fun exploring new places?

Do you like to read lots of books? **Y**

N

Do you love to organise fun things to do with your friends?

N

N

Do you enjoy doing things on your own? **N**

Is dancing your favourite thing to do at a party?

Y

Y

Y

N

N

Do you like to get up early in the morning?

N

Y

Y

Do you have a large group of friends? **N**

Do you love to follow the latest fashion trends?

Do you think you are quite a busy person?

N

Y

Y

N

Y

Belinda the Butterfly Fish

You are most like Belinda the Butterfly Fish. You love nothing more than going to your friends' parties and you are always the first person to organise a sleepover. You are happiest when you have all of your friends together in one place and are having a great time!

Coraline the Shrimp

You are most like Coraline the Shrimp. You are always busy and like to have a few good friends that you can rely on, rather than being in a large group. You enjoy being a bit different to everybody else and love having your own individual style rather than following trends.

How many small seashells can you count on the sand?

Write the answer in the box.

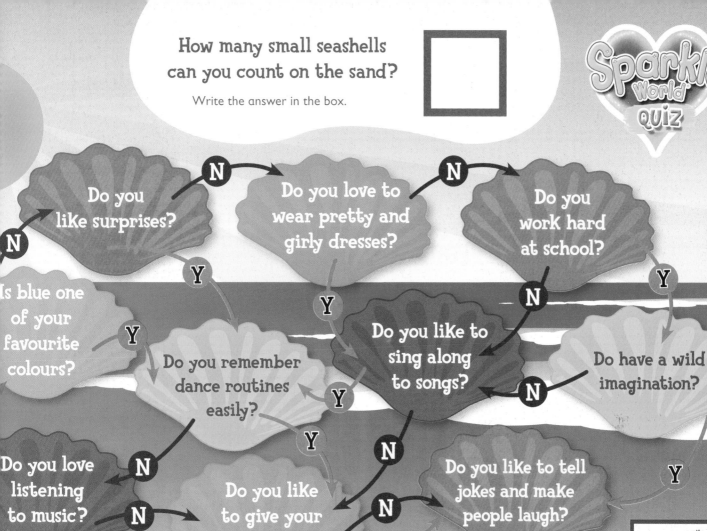

N Do you like surprises?

N Do you love to wear pretty and girly dresses?

N Do you work hard at school?

Is blue one of your favourite colours?

Do you remember dance routines easily?

Do you like to sing along to songs?

Do have a wild imagination?

Do you love listening to music?

Do you like to give your friends advice?

Do you like to tell jokes and make people laugh?

Are you sometimes shy when meeting new people?

Are you good at keeping secrets?

Pocketville®
Play With Your Pets ONLINE!
www.oceaninmypocket.co.uk

Tess the Dolphin

You are most like Tess the Dolphin. You love to dance and perform routines that you have learned. Your friends always come to you when they need cheering up and trust your good advice. You are a very happy and bubbly person that others love to be around.

Teaser the Turtle

You are most like Teaser the Marine Turtle. You love to try lots of different things and enjoy exploring new places. You can sometimes be a little bit shy, but you love nothing more than to play practical jokes and make people happy. Your friends think you're funny!

© 2011 MEG; Ocean In My Pocket ® is a registered trademark; ALL RIGHTS RESERVED.

Sky the Blue Fairy

Read the story below. When you see a picture, say the word instead.

Sky

and were friends of the fairies! One day, asked for their

help finding the Rainbow Fairies. had banished them from Fairyland

and trapped them on Rainspell Island. gave and magic bags

to help them and they set off to look for the fairies. They were searching the

beach, when a tiny scuttled out from under a clump of seaweed.

"Fairy in trouble!" muttered the . "Did you hear that?" gasped.

The led the girls to a shimmering . A huge bubble

floated to the surface and inside was the Blue Fairy! "Please help me!"

cried . Suddenly, there was a cracking sound and the

froze over! Two ugly skated across the ice! had sent the

to stop the fairy escaping! "Hee, hee, the fairy can't get out!" laughed

one of the . Then remembered her magic bag. She reached

inside and found a tiny blue stone. It was hot! threw it in the

72 www.mysparkleworld.com

goblins

Rachel

King Oberon and Queen Titania

Kirsty

crab

rock pool

Jack Frost

and the ice melted! "Ouch! Hot!" yelled the , rushing away.  popped the bubble and helped  out of the water. Then they took her to a safe hiding place in the woods. "Thank you so much,  and ," smiled .

© 2011 Rainbow Magic Limited. A HIT Entertainment Company.

Let's Play Bingo!

You and your friends will love playing bingo with the puppies, fairies and other magical creatures from the Enchanted Valley!

Puppy in my Pocket®
Enchanted Valley

Summer
2

Tickles
3

Jade
4

Winston
5

Ruby
6

Ben
7

Wizzy
Alaskan

Sassy
Beagle

You will need: 1-3 friends to play with, a pen for each player and 2 dice.

How to play: Each player chooses to play with either Wizzy, Sassy, Dickens or Blossom. Take it in turns to roll the dice. Check which picture along the rainbow matches the number thrown. If a player has the same picture, she should cross it out. Play until one player has crossed out all her pictures. Shout "Bingo!" to win the game.

Goldie
8

Sparkles
9

Grace
10

Penny
11

Stardust
12

Blossom
Spaniel

Dickens
Boxer

© 2011 MEG: Puppy In My Pocket® and Enchanted Valley® are registered trademarks. ALL RIGHTS RESERVED.

Pocketville
Play With Your Pets ONLINE!
www.puppyinmypocket.co.uk

Tropical Falls

Rainforest Friends!

How well do you know your Rainforest In My Pocket friends? To find out, read the clues in the circles, then match each one to the correct animal. When you are sure you know the answer, write the correct letter in the butterfly shapes.

A

I'm a Parrot Fish. My scales are lots of different colours and I shimmer in the sunlight! I like to play hide and seek!

Floss

B

I'm a Kiwi Bird but I'm not like most other birds because I can't fly! That doesn't stop me from having lots of fun though. I often wait on the ground and catch falling fruit that my rainforest friends shake from the trees.

G

C

I'm a Lorikeet which is a type of parrot and I have extremely colourful feathers! I always wear my mask and flippers when I swim!

E

Vanilla

D

I am a Chameleon and I can do a really cool trick! I can make each of my eyes look in different directions!

B

Kira

Answers: A. Poppy; B. Kira; C. Pina; D. Cameo; E. Vanilla; F. Sunny; G. Floss.

Pina

F I am a very exotic looking animal called a Mandrill. I have a large red nose and blue streaks down each side of my face. I love to drink banana smoothies.

Pocketville
Play With Your Pets ONLINE!
www.rainforestinmypocket.co.uk

E I am an Anteater. I love flowers and enjoy exploring the rainforest looking for new ones. You'll always recognise me by my pink hat and flower necklace.

D

Cameo

Sunny

F

G I am a Sugar Glider. I love eucalyptus leaves almost as much as my favourite treat - candy floss. I fly from tree to tree and I have large flaps of skin between all four of my legs that help me to float like a parachute.

Pappy

A

© 2011 MEG; Rainforest In My Pocket® is a registered trademark. ALL RIGHTS RESERVED.

Colouring Time!

Colour the picture of Strawberry Shortcake, Plum Pudding, Orange Blossom and the Berrykins, using the small picture to help you.

The bow on Strawberry's basket is blue.

Tick the correct box.

True ☐   False ☑

![my LITTLE PONY]

It was a beautiful day in the land of Equestria. In the little town of Ponyville, all the ponies were out shopping and chatting with friends. All except Twilight Sparkle. She was much too busy!

Princess Celestia had sent Twilight Sparkle and her assistant, Spike, to Ponyville to learn about friendship. Now the Princess was coming to find out if she had learned anything new.

"Oh, Spike!" wailed Twilight Sparkle. "I haven't learned anything new lately. And before the Princess gets here we have to make sure the town looks perfect!"

"Don't worry! I'm on it!" said Spike, dashing around as he gathered up books. Suddenly, he tripped up and the books tumbled everywhere.

"Oopsie!" groaned Spike.

"We need help," declared Twilight Sparkle. And she knew exactly who to ask! Her new best friends, Rainbow Dash, Pinkie Pie, Fluttershy, Applejack and Rarity.

Twilight Sparkle soon found her friends chatting outside the sweet shop.

"Hi, ponies," said Twilight Sparkle. "I really need your help! Princess Celestia is visiting today…"

"Excuse me!" said Pinkie Pie. "I need to buy cakes!" And she dashed into the sweet shop!

"Wow! Must fly!" cried Rainbow Dash, shooting into the sky.

"I need my hairbrush!" squealed Rarity, skipping away.

"See you all later, guys!" said Applejack, galloping off in a cloud of dust.

As for Fluttershy, she mumbled something so quiet Twilight Sparkle couldn't hear it, then skipped away too!

"I guess my friends are too busy," sighed Twilight Sparkle. As she walked home, she looked up and saw rain clouds in the sky. The royal visit was turning into a disaster!

Twilight Sparkle raced around cleaning up the library. Then she looked at the time. "Oh, no," she cried.

© 2011 Hasbro. All Rights Reserved.

Princess Celestia is planning a royal visit, but how will Twilight Sparkle get Ponyville ready all on her own?

Sparkle World story

"Princess Celestia will be here any moment. And I haven't even brushed my hair, or made the town look nice!"

She stepped outside, and gasped in amazement! Rainbow Dash was whizzing around the sky clearing away the clouds. Applejack had brought baskets of shiny red apples, and Pinkie Pie had created a tea party. And Fluttershy had brought a kaleidoscope of butterflies to welcome the princess.

"Aha, there you are!" cried Rarity, dashing up to Twilight Sparkle. "You can't possibly greet the Princess with your hair looking like that!"

With a few flicks of her brush, she made Twilight Sparkle's hair look glossy and neat. Just in time!

A few seconds later, Princess Celestia flew into town.

"What a wonderful welcome!" smiled Princess Celestia. "Have you learned anything new about friendship, Twilight Sparkle?"

"Not really…" began Twilight Sparkle. And then she looked around at everything her friends had done to help. "… except never to lose faith in your friends, because true friends are always there when you need them!"

"Splendid!" beamed the Princess. "Your friends sound truly wonderful!"

Twilight Sparkle smiled.

"You're absolutely right," she said. "They are!"

Lea

Which accessories would complete Polly's look?

sunglasses

bag

necklace

bangles

earrings

Now draw a picture of Polly wearing her rockin' party outfit.

Sparkle World Design

Sparkle World®
crafts & recipes!

Let's have a... Pink Party!
The Sparkle Girls have lots of ideas to help you!

Invitations

You'll need to tell all your friends your plans! Don't forget to include the date, time and venue on your invitations. Feeling creative? You can make your own invitations or why not download The Sparkle Girls' fab pink invitations from the Sparkle World website?

www.mysparkleworld.com

A cool idea would be to write the details of your party on self-adhesive labels and stick each one to a lollipop! Yummy and fun!

Princess Bug Place cards
Lou

You will need: pink craft foam, googly eyes, pink furry balls, a paper doily and white paper.

Ask an adult to help you cut a heart shape from the craft foam. Stick a furry ball on the heart to make feet. Attach two googly eyes. Stick the bug on a strip paper with your guest's name on it. Using a small sect of a paper doily, give your princess bug a tiara!

Let's make... Shortbread Wands!

Ask an adult to preheat the oven to 200°C or gas mark 6.

Ingredients:
275g plain flour
200g firm butter, diced
100g icing sugar
2 egg yolks
20 lolly sticks

To decorate:
1 egg white
sugar crystal decorations

1. Place the flour and butter in a bowl and rub together until it makes crumbs.

2. Stir in the icing sugar, then add the egg yolks and squeeze the mixture together to make a dough. Roll out on a lightly floured work surface and cut into 20 stars, about 8-9cm across at the widest point.

3. Place on a baking tray and carefully push a lolly stick into each star. Bake for 6-8 minutes until just turning golden brown at the edges.

4. When the biscuits are cooked, brush them very lightly with egg white.

5. Sprinkle with sugar crystals and leave them to cool for 10 minutes before removing from the baking tray. Tie a bow with ribbon around each stick.

Ask your guests to wear something pink!

My Sparkle World .com

Party bags

Everyone loves a party bag to take home, so spoil your friends with a bag bursting with pink treats! Our ideas for things you could include are sweets, lip gloss, pink foil-wrapped chocolate hearts, hair bobbles, pens or pencils, mini chocolate bars, jewellery, stickers, badges, bubbles, bead kits, purses, face paints or key rings.

Tie cutlery together with ribbon. Paper doilies add a pretty effect!

Pink treats could include marshmallows, bonbons, pink wafer biscuits and strawberries!

Strawberry milkshake served in cocktail glasses adds a touch of glamour!

Thank you cards

When the party's over, don't forget to thank your friends for coming and for any gifts you may have received. You could hand write your thank you letters, or you could finish off your pink party with the perfect thank you notes, downloaded from www.mysparkleworld.com.

Decorate the table with jewels and tiaras for your guests. Don't forget place cards, napkins and streamers!

Louise

Decorate the table with streamers!

Strawberries and watermelon make delicious party treats!

Marshmallows and strawberry bonbons are yummy!

© 2011 Redan.

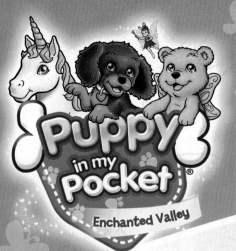

An Enchanted Discovery!

The Enchanted Valley friends will help you discover what to do with your future! How to play: Stare at each of the rainbow circles that contain an enchanted friend for 30 seconds. Close your eyes. When you open them again, the friend that jumps out at you first will reveal their suggestion.

Tickles

Penny

Benny

Winston

Dapper

Sparkles

© 2011 MEG; Puppy In My Pocket® and Enchanted Valley are registered trademarks. ALL RIGHTS RESERVED.

Pocketville
Play With Your Pets ONLINE!
www.puppyinmypocket.co.uk

True or false?

There are five green stars on these pages.
Tick the correct box.

| T ✓ | F |

Tickles

You are very talented and enjoy meeting new people. You like to make your friends laugh, a bit like Tickles! Plan a party for your friends so you have a chance to be a good host and entertain everybody.

Penny

You love to listen to your friends' problems and offer them good advice. Like Penny, you can chat to friends for hours and forget the time! Why not invite a friend to your house for a catch up?

Sparkles

Just like Sparkles, you enjoy travelling to new and exciting places! You are always on the go and don't like to sit still for long. Try a new sport or hobby with a friend. You have more than enough energy for it!

Winston

You are a deep thinker like Winston. You don't rush into decisions and you always consider other people. Start writing a diary or make a scrapbook to keep a special record of your thoughts, memories and plans!

Dapper

You are a very playful person. You love playing games on your own or with friends. You can be very competitive, but don't mind losing at things either. Why not start a game of hide and seek right now?

Benny

Just like Benny, you love to sing and dance. You know dance moves to all of your favourite songs! You are happiest when you are performing for friends or in a show. You should try joining theatre club.

Netty   Hugo   Bumpy

Read the story. When you see a picture, say the word instead.

How many turtles?

4

Write the number in the box.

 wanted to visit her friend at the other end of

the Coral Reef. But it was too far to take her babies. "Will you

look after , and  ?"

asked  . "Of course," smiled . She

wasn't used to looking after baby turtles, but didn't think it

would be too hard! "How about a game?" asked

 , once had gone. "Okay!" agreed

 , fetching his  .  flipped the

but it went so far it disappeared altogether! "Oops!" said

 . "Let's play hide and seek instead!" But every

time tried to hide in the , the babies

88 www.mysparkleworld.com

© 2011 MEG; Ocean In My Pocket® is a registered trademark.
ALL RIGHTS RESERVED.

Pocketville
Play With Your Pets ONLINE!
www.oceaninmypocket.co.uk

Cleopatra

Sonia

ball

bubbles

seaweed

spotted her straight away.  was bigger than anything! "We're bored," sighed . But  was running out of ideas! "Hey, want to see a trick?" said . She swam up to the surface, leapt out of the water and dived back in with a mighty splash! ,  and  were tossed about in a swirling cloud of !

"Oh, no, that wasn't supposed to happen!"  gasped. But to her surprise, the babies were laughing. "Do it again!" giggled . So she did. By the time she came back, 's babies were tired but very happy.  wasn't just the biggest babysitter ever. She was the BEST!

We had a whale of a time!

The bubbles tickled!

Cleopatra is the best babysitter!

Fairy Code!

Sky and Izzy have a secret word for you to discover!
Put a letter in each flower shape to make two words.

RIVE **r** AIN
BANAN **a** UTUMN
SAFAR **i** NDIGO
ACOR **n** IGHT
THUM **b** UBBLES
TOMAT **o** RANGE
HOLLO **w** AND

r a i n b o w

Write the letters here.

Sky
the Blue Fairy

Izzy
the Indigo Fairy

Count the symbols and write the answer to the sum in the flower shape.

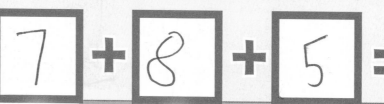

$$7 + 8 + 5 = 20$$

*   ★   ♥

 © 2011 Rainbow Magic Limited. A HIT Entertainment Company.

Advertisement

Polly's Fab Memory Game!

Test your memory skills with Polly in this cool game! Good luck!

Player 1 ① ② ③ ④ ⑤ ⑥ ⑦ ⑧ ⑨

Shani

Lila

Polly

Kerstie

Rick

Lea

Crissy

Disco Bat

Meowmallow

www.mysparkleworld.com

Check out www.pollypocket.co.uk

You will need: 2 players, 2 pens and 18 circles of card, to cover all of the pictures below.

How to play: Cover all of the pictures with the circles of card. Take it in turns to uncover one picture from each page. If the pictures match, keep the pieces of card and colour a flower, then have another go! If the pictures don't match, cover them over again, then the other player takes her turn. The first player to colour all of her flowers is the winner.

Player 2 ❀1 ❀2 ❀3 ❀4 ❀5 ❀6 ❀7 ❀8 ❀9

Lea

Crissy

Kerstie

Disco Bat

Polly

Meowmallow

Rick

Shani

Lila

© 2011 Mattel, Inc. All Rights Reserved.
© 2011 Origin Products Limited.